CLASSIC LAN

MORECAMBE
BAY

CLASSIC LANDFORMS OF

MORECAMBE BAY

S J GALE

University of Sydney

Series editors
Rodney Castleden and Christopher Green

Published by the Geographical Association
in conjunction with the
British Geomorphological Research Group

Geographical
Association

THE BRITISH GEOMORPHOLOGICAL RESEARCH GROUP

PREFACE

Geomorphologists study landforms and the processes that create and modify them. The results of their work, published as they invariably are in specialist journals, usually remain inaccessible to the general public. We should like to put that right. Scattered across the landscapes of England, Wales, Scotland and Ireland there are many beautiful and striking landforms which delight the eye of the general public and are visited by educational parties from schools, colleges and universities. Our aim in producing this series of guides is to make modern explanations of these classic landforms available to all, in a style and format that will be easy to use in the field. We hope that an informed understanding of the origins of these features will help the visitor to enjoy the landscape all the more.

Encouraged by the success of the first editions of the Classic Landform Guides we are pleased to introduce this new series with some additional titles, enhanced by colour photographs, new illustrations and with the valuable addition of 1:50 000 map extracts by kind permission of the Education Team, Ordnance Survey. The relevant maps for the area covered in this book are Ordnance Survey 1:50 000 Landranger Series, sheets 96 and 97. Please refer to the current Ordnance Survey Index for details of the relevant 1:25 000 sheets.

Rodney Castleden *Roedean School, Brighton*
Christopher Green *Royal Holloway, University of London*

ISBN 1 899085 63 7
This edition first published 2000
Published by the Geographical Association, 160 Solly Street, Sheffield S1 4BF.
The views expressed in this publication are those of the author and do not necessarily
represent those of the Geographical Association.
The Geographical Association is a registered charity no. 313129.
Cover photograph: Whitbarrow. *Photo:* Stephen Gale.
Frontispiece: Hutton Roof Crags. *Photo:* Stephen Gale.

CONTENTS

Acknowledgements

he author would like to acknowledge The University of New England for granting the
ical leave which enabled this book to be written, and Professor I. Douglas for providing
o the facilities of the Department of Geography, The University of Manchester whilst this
was being undertaken. He would also like to thank Mrs E. Gale, Mr F.J. Gale, Mr R.J.B.
Miss E.A. Smith and Professor H.P.M. Winchester for their help with the fieldwork. He is
arly grateful to Professor Winchester for reading and commenting on an earlier version of
this text and to Mr P.R. Johnson for drafting many of the figures.
ing reproduced from Ordnance Survey 1:50 000 Landranger mapping with the permission
of The Controller of The Stationery Office © Crown Copyright 82324M 01/2000
Copy Editing: Kath Davies, Edinburgh
Illustrations: Paul Coles, Sheffield, and Peter Johnson, Sydney
Series design concept: Quarto Design, Huddersfield
Design and typesetting: ATG Design, Catalyst Creative Imaging, Leeds
Printed and binding: Colorcraft Limited, Hong Kong

INTRODUCTION

The **karst** of the Morecambe Bay region of north-west England is developed on an almost continuous belt of Carboniferous limestone which fringes the southern edge of the Lake District and extends from Millom in the west to the Lune valley in the east (Figures 1 and 2). The landscape of the region is characterised by a series of upstanding, fault-bound limestone blocks. Within the Millom, Low Furness and Kellet districts, most of the limestone is blanketed by glacial deposits. Elsewhere, however, much of the bedrock is exposed and supports a spectacular series of steep-sided hills which stand proud of the low-lying landscape of the Bay and its associated **mosses**.

The Morecambe Bay area possesses a range of classic karst features. The **limestone pavements** of Hutton Roof Crags are world-renowned and caves such as Kirkhead have gained an international reputation because of the archaeological remains they contain. The area possesses probably the greatest assemblage of large **dolines** known in

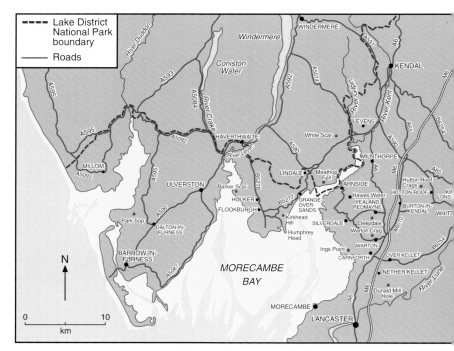

Figure 1: The Morecambe Bay area: *location and access.*

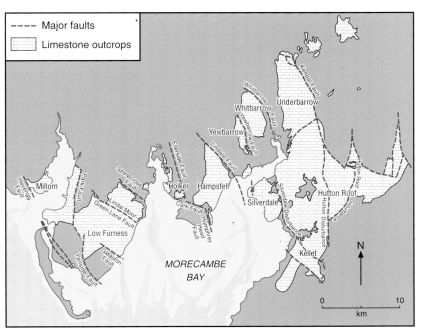

Figure 2: The Morecambe Bay karst showing the location of the major geological structures.

the British Isles, as well as rare British examples of true karst **poljes**. Research on the karst of the Morecambe Bay area has shown that the impact of glacial erosion on the landscape of south Cumbria is far less than is conventionally believed, whilst the age of much of the landscape is far greater than has previously been accepted. The area also contains impressive, though rarely described, examples of sinking streams and **blind valleys**, and landforms which throw light on the contentious issue of high sea-levels during the Quaternary.

GEOLOGY

The rocks of the Morecambe Bay district have been investigated by a succession of distinguished geologists, beginning with the Reverend Adam Sedgwick in the early years of the nineteenth century. The most recent and most accessible reviews of the geological history of the area are those of the Institute of Geological Sciences (Rose and Dunham, 1977) and Professor Moseley (1978), and much of this section is based on their work.

The Carboniferous rocks of the Morecambe Bay area were deposited unconformably on a sequence of mudstones, siltstones and sandstones of Silurian age (Table 1). The lowest deposits in the Carboniferous succession are the mainly **clastic** Basement Beds and it is only towards the top of this formation that limestones become predominant (Table 2). The Basement Beds are succeeded by five dominantly calcareous units – the Martin Limestone, Red Hill Oolite, Dalton Beds, Park Limestone and Urswick Limestone – each of which possesses a distinctive lithology. These units are overlain by

Table 1: The chronology of tectonic and geomorphic events in the Morecambe Bay karst

Age (million years)	Period or sub-era	Major tectonic events	Episodes of karstification
	Quaternary		Quaternary karstification
2			
	Tertiary	?Mid-Tertiary uplift and reactivation of faults	?Mid-Tertiary karstification
65			
	Cretaceous		
146			
	Jurassic		
208			
	Triassic		
245			
	Permian		
			Permo-Carboniferous karstification
290			
	Carboniferous	End-Carboniferous Hercynian earth movements	Early Carboniferous karstification
363			
	Devonian		
409			
	Silurian	End-Silurian Caledonian earth movements	
439			
	Ordovician		

8

the largely clastic deposits of the Gleaston Formation and the Roosecote Mudstones. Limestones tend to occur only in the lower part of the Gleaston Formation and are effectively absent from the Roosecote Mudstones.

The Roosecote Mudstones appear to be restricted to the western part of the region. To the east, their correlatives seem to be the sandstones that crop out at Ings Point (SD 479723) and throughout the Kellet area. These mudstones and sandstones are of early Late Carboniferous age and represent the youngest Carboniferous rocks in the Morecambe Bay area. The absence of younger Late Carboniferous rocks from the region is the result of erosion rather than non-deposition, for outliers of Late Carboniferous strata in north west Yorkshire bear witness to the former continuity of these beds across the Morecambe Bay area.

Table 2: The chronology, stratigraphy and lithology of Carboniferous rocks in the Morecambe Bay area

Age (million years)	Unit	Lithology
	Roosecote Mudstones	Mudstones and siltstones with occasional sandstones and rare limestones.
333	Gleaston Formation	A highly variable and complex unit of shales, mudstones, sandstones and limestones. The limestones are pale grey to black, medium to massively bedded often cherty and contain abundant beds and partings of shale.
336	Urswick Limestone	Hard, compact, white to dark grey limestones, with a range of textures including skeletal fragments in a finer matrix, sands and **pseudobreccias**. The unit is widely jointed and thickly to massively bedded, with beds varying from 0.5m to 5m thick. The beds are commonly separated by thin partings of shale. The Woodbine Shale, a dark grey, 4.5m thick bed, lies about 30m above the base of the formation.
339	Park Limestone	Cream or pale grey limestones, typically composed of carbonate sands, frequently in a muddy matrix. Generally massively bedded and closely jointed.
343	Dalton Beds	Dark grey, medium to thickly bedded, medium jointed and medium grained muddy limestones. Beds are generally up to 1m thick, although they are thinly bedded in the middle of the unit. The well-marked undulatory bedding planes possess thin partings of calcareous shale. The upper part of the unit is frequently **dolomitised**.
345	Red Hill Oolite	Thickly to massively bedded and closely jointed pale limestones, typically composed of rounded carbonate sands. Common shale partings.
	Martin Limestone	Grey or greenish grey, hard, compact, fine grained limestones, containing abundant partings and beds of calcareous shale. Medium to thickly bedded and medium to widely jointed. Some **dolomitisation**.
	Basement Beds	Shales, mudstones, sandstones and conglomerates, containing some thin and impure limestones and occasional thin gypsums.

Cumbria as a whole appears to have been significantly affected only by the end-Carboniferous phase of the Hercynian Orogeny (Table 1). In the Morecambe Bay area, these earth movements gave rise to a series of north to south-trending monoclinal folds (Figure 2):

1. The Silverdale Disturbance.
2. The Hutton Disturbance-Kendal Fault.
3. The Hutton Roof Disturbance.

In the northern part of the area, a series of north to south faults with westerly downthrows and general easterly dips may represent the northward continuation of these fold belts. Sets of faults aligned north-west to south-east and north-east to south-west may also be attributed to the Hercynian Orogeny.

The Hercynian earth movements appear to have initiated a major phase of denudation which resulted in the almost total removal of Late Carboniferous beds from the Morecambe Bay area. Erosion cut down deeply into the limestones, in places exposing rocks as low in the succession as the Red Hill Oolite.

In the Early Permian (Table 1), a thin and discontinuous **breccia** was deposited on the eroded Carboniferous basement. The gravel-strewn surface was briefly and partially submerged during the Late Permian by rising sea-levels. A thin sequence of dark mudstones and siltstones was deposited and a dolomite was precipitated around the margins of the sea. The environment subsequently became more saline and a series of red mudstones and siltstones was laid down. This merges gradually upwards into the Triassic St Bees Sandstone, which consists of several hundred metres of red, largely fluvial, sandstones. The sandstones are finally succeeded by some 550m of mudstones interbedded with rock salt. The Permo-Triassic rocks of the area are now restricted to the western part of the region, although it is likely that the Triassic rocks at least were originally laid down throughout the Morecambe Bay area.

The most recent orogenic phase to have influenced the region occurred sometime after the Triassic (Table 1). The principal effects of this were the reactivation of existing faults and the uplift of the Lake District and Pennine massifs. The north-west to south-east faults were particularly active, having displacements of several hundred metres in some situations.

With the exception of those features associated with post-Triassic mineralisation, there is little evidence either in the Morecambe Bay area or throughout Cumbria as a whole for geological events between the Triassic and the Quaternary. The uplifting of the Lake District (and Morecambe Bay marginal to it) initiated an episode of erosion which may have continued to the present day. However, several workers have suggested that Jurassic, Cretaceous and, possibly, Tertiary rocks were deposited across Cumbria, and there is a long-standing belief that the drainage pattern radiating out from central Cumbria was developed upon an updomed cover of Cretaceous chalk.

Geology exerts a profound influence on the landscape of the

Morecambe Bay karst. The monoclinal folds and major faults provide the primary control on geomorphology, influencing the location and morphology of major karst features such as sops (page 17), poljes (page 35) and dolines (page 28), as well as the overall distribution of high and low ground in the area. Lithological variations are also of significance. The Urswick Limestone, for example, constitutes the most important karst lithology in the Morecambe Bay area, possessing about half the known caves and all the well developed limestone pavements (page 37). By contrast, whilst pavements are rare on the Red Hill Oolite and the Park Limestone, the sops are preferentially developed in these units (Figure 3).

GEOMORPHOLOGICAL HISTORY

Carboniferous karstification

Relative falls in sea-level during the deposition of the Carboniferous limestone may have been sufficient to expose the rock to sub-aerial processes and cause karstification. The most convincing evidence of this comes from the presence of **palaeokarst surfaces.** These can be found in a number of places in the limestone sequence, but amongst the best examples is that at Barker Scar (SD 333782) in the Holker district, where mammillated surfaces with a relief of 1-2cm and a wavelength of 2-4cm are found close to the base of unit i of the Dalton Beds (Photo 1). The surfaces are exactly mirrored by the base of the bed above and there can be no doubt that they pre-date the deposition of the overlying limestone. The absence of notable grike (page 41) development is presumably the result of the occurrence of erosion prior to the formation of joints in the rock, possibly even in largely unlithified carbonate sediment. These and similar features elsewhere represent the earliest evidence of karstification in the Morecambe Bay area.

Photo 1: Palaeokarst surfaces close to the base of unit i of the Early Carboniferous Dalton Beds, Barker Scar. Each of the units in this exposure is labelled with a letter. The lens cap is 50mm in diameter. Photo: Stephen Gale.

Permo-Carboniferous karstification

The limestone was next exposed to sub-aerial processes during the Permo-Carboniferous when erosion consequent upon Late Carboniferous tectonic activity removed hundreds of metres of non-calcareous sediments from above the limestone (Table 1). Despite the speculations of several authors, there is no conclusive evidence of karstification at this time, although geomorphological and hydrological conditions are likely to have been favourable for this, at least during the early part of the period.

?Tertiary karstification

At some stage after the Triassic, the Morecambe Bay region experienced a major phase of karstification (Table 1). The evidence for this lies in the extensive exhumed karst found in Low Furness, along with similar features in the Silverdale area. The exhumed karst is almost invariably associated with deposits of hematite (a form of iron oxide). Some of the hematite occurs in veins and flats, but most was deposited in solutionally-eroded features in the Carboniferous limestone known as sops (Figure 3 and Photo 2). Much of the work on the sops reported here is the product of the inter-war re-survey of the Furness iron ore field undertaken by William Rose and Sir Kingsley Dunham (1977).

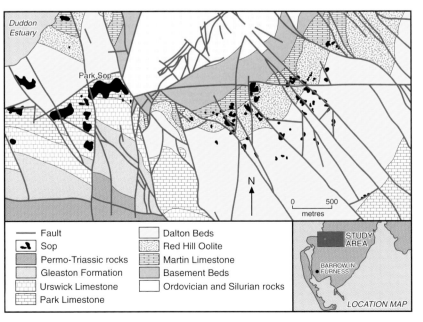

Figure 3: The geology of Low Furness showing the location of the sops. After: Rose and Dunham, 1977; Rose et al., 1977.

Photo 2: Park Sop, Dalton-in-Furness *(SD 212755) in 1938. Following removal of the ore, subsidence has exposed the limestone walls of the sop. Photo:IPR/24-29 British Geological Survey. © NERC.*

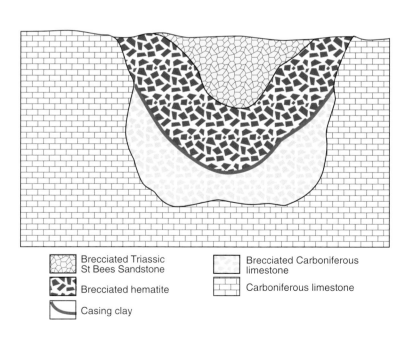

Figure 4: Schematic cross-section through a typical Morecambe Bay sop. *After: Rose and Dunham, 1977.*

The sops are circular to oval, basin-like features, narrowing downwards into deep pockets. With the exception of a few sites where sops are developed along a fault and where one side is composed of a different rock, these features occur only in limestone (Figure 3). The sops appear to have formed only where the St Bees Sandstone rested directly on Carboniferous limestone and they are absent where Carboniferous and Permian mudstones and siltstones lie between the limestone and the sandstone. The largest sop, Park (SD 2175), is 420m long, 20-180m wide and reaches a maximum depth of 180m. From this, there is a gradation in size down to sops only 30m wide and less than 30m deep.

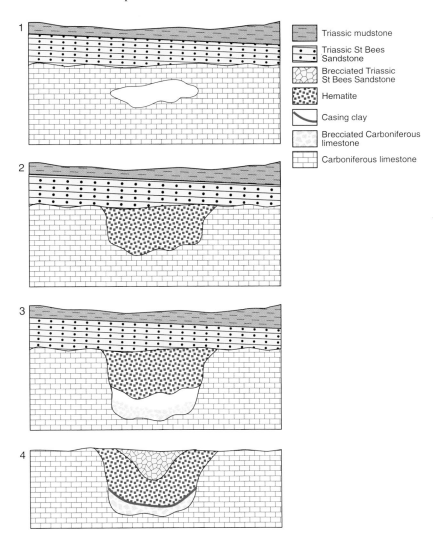

Figure 5: Hypothesised stages in the formation of sops. After: Rose and Dunham, 1977.

The sops possess a characteristic depositional sequence, though not all members are necessarily present in each case (Figure 4). The lowest bed is a collapse deposit of water-worn limestone blocks. The **interstices** between the blocks are infilled by fine-grained clastic deposits. The collapse breccia is overlain by the casing, a bright red, **slickensided** clay, 0.1-1m thick, containing angular fragments of hematite. The next layer, the ore, consists of a mass of broken fragments and blocks of iron oxides, with quartz and occasional manganese oxides set in a red, powdery hematite or black, manganiferous matrix. Finally, in the largest sops, a central core of large blocks, indistinguishable from the St Bees Sandstone, occurs. Although almost all the sops are associated with hematite and mineralisation, at least two hollows contain sandstone but no ore.

The most convincing explanation of the features observed in the sops is that pre-existing karstic voids (perhaps formed during the episode of exposure of the limestone in the Permo-Carboniferous) were mineralised by downward-percolating, iron-rich waters (Figure 5, stages 1 and 2). These fluids could have gained access to the karst only in locations where the St Bees Sandstone directly overlay the limestone. Effluent mineralising waters may have focused solution beneath the hematite body. Alternatively, conventional groundwater flow may have been concentrated around the impermeable mass of the ore. In either case, the resultant cavities would have collapsed to produce a breccia of unaltered limestone (Figure 5, stage 3). Fine-grained clastic sediments transported by groundwater flow would

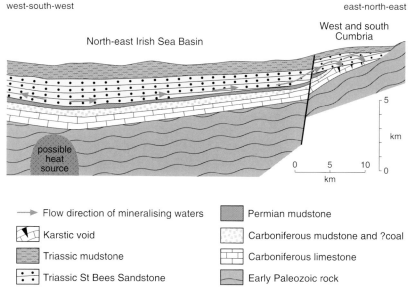

Figure 6: Schematic cross-section through the north-east Irish Sea Basin showing *the possible source and direction of flow of the mineralising waters which deposited the iron in the Morecambe Bay area. After: Rose and Dunham, 1977.*

have been deposited in the cavities, both before and after collapse. The ore body would have been let down into the underlying void, providing a cavity for the collapse of the St Bees Sandstone. The casing may have resulted from the transport of fines suspended in waters percolating through the ore body. Slickensiding in the casing may have been caused by further collapse and settling of the basal breccia (Figure 5, stage 4).

Tiny inclusions of fluid from calcites intimately associated with the hematite have been analysed. The results indicate temperatures of approximately 84-110°C during the closing stages of mineralisation and salinities from four to six times those of sea water. These findings appear to rule out mineralisation from downward-percolating meteoric waters: the calcites (and presumably the iron oxides and the quartz) must therefore have been deposited from hypersaline brines. How can these findings be reconciled with the model of ore deposition given above? Rose and Dunham (1977) proposed a mechanism of mineralisation whereby hypersaline fluids were driven up-dip along beds of the permeable St Bees Sandstone from a heat source in the north-east Irish Sea Basin (Figure 6). Leaching of the St Bees Sandstone would have provided the necessary quantities of iron. When the warm, iron-rich brines reached places in west and south Cumbria where they had free access to fractures, replaceable limestones and karst features, they descended into the limestones to form the ore deposits.

Many of the ore bodies are associated with post-Triassic faults. Yet none of the bodies is brecciated against such faults and they cross the faults without displacement (Figure 3). The mineralisation (and thus the re-initiation of karstification) therefore post-dates the post-Triassic faulting. In central and northern England, a mid-Tertiary age is usually assigned to faults that displace Triassic to Cretaceous strata (Table 1). However, the possibility of earlier fracturing cannot be ignored, for there is a continuous history of pulsed tectonism in northern England from Hercynian times to the present. The formation of the sops must also have pre-dated the removal of the St Bees Sandstone from most of the Morecambe Bay area.

Both the karstification and the mineralisation of the sops may have been associated with the episode of tectonic activity that caused the faulting. Fracturing may have provided fissures for groundwater movement, uplift may have resulted in greater hydraulic gradients and increased denudation may have allowed the circulation of meteoric waters through the limestone. Furthermore, tectonic pressures may have driven iron-rich waters up-dip from the north-east Irish Sea Basin. The most likely age for the formation of the sops of the Morecambe Bay area, therefore, is mid-Tertiary, though both earlier and later dates are possible.

Further phases of karstification in the Morecambe Bay area during the Tertiary have been proposed. In 1957, Professor Corbel compared the isolated limestone hills which emerge from the mosses of the area to a tropical tower karst landscape (Photo 3). He regarded the hills as

Photo 3: Meathop Fell *(SD 4379) from the west. This limestone hill was interpreted by Professor Corbel (1957) as a relict of tropical humid karstification during the Tertiary. In fact, the isolated nature of the hill is a result of structural control. It is bounded by the Lindale Fault to the west and the Yewbarrow Fault to the east (Figure 2). Photo: Stephen Gale.*

relict from a warm humid phase of the Tertiary. In fact, the isolated nature of the limestone uplands is largely a result of structural control (Figure 2) and there is no evidence for the operation of karst tower-foot processes around the base of the hills.

Dr Sweeting (1970, 1972, 1973) supported the hypothesis of karstification under relatively warm climatic conditions, probably in the Tertiary. Her evidence included:

1. The presence of **rock pendants** in the caves.
2. The existence of reddish soil or clay of a **terra rossa** type.
3. The occurrence of apparently solutionally-eroded slopes beneath the fossil screes of the area.

However, the rock pendants in the caves are simply the result of differential solution and are not indicative of specific climatic conditions. Furthermore, most of the red sediments found on the limestone are glacial in origin, their colour derived either from the red Permo-Triassic rocks of the area or from hematite reworked from the countless mineralised fractures and beds in the region. Elsewhere, the red deposits consist of hematite-stained **loess** (Vincent, 1981). Finally, the rock slopes found beneath the fossil screes of the Morecambe Bay area are glacially rather than solutionally modified. An excellent example of this may be seen at White Scar (SD 460852) on the southern side of Whitbarrow. Here quarrying of cemented limestone scree has revealed a glacially-striated limestone bedding plane

18

Photo 4: The glacially-scoured bedding plane bench at White Scar, Whitbarrow
(SD 460852). The bench has been exposed as a result of the quarrying of overlying till and cemented scree. An impressive array of brachiopod (Productus) *shells stands proud of the bedding plane as a result of differential solution. Photo: Stephen Gale.*

(Photos 4 and 5). Vertically-aligned striations on the limestone cliff backing the bedding plane have also been exposed as a result of the quarrying. During the last glacial, ice at this point presumably flowed south directly over the southern end of Whitbarrow.

There is thus no evidence to support the thesis of sub-aerial karstification in the Morecambe Bay area during the Tertiary. Indeed, although the limestone to the east of the area may have been exposed to sub-aerial processes during this period, the evidence of mineralisation in the Silverdale area suggests that, as with the west, the karst remained buried beneath Permo-Triassic beds until at least the mid-Tertiary.

Photo 5: Striations on the bedrock bench at White Scar, Whitbarrow (SD 460852).
This photograph was taken in 1978 and these striae have since been weathered away
*by aggressive **sheetflows**. However, bedrock striations can still be found preserved*
beneath the calcareous till and cemented scree which elsewhere overlie the bedrock.
Photo: Stephen Gale.

Access

To reach Barker Scar, take the B5278 south from the A590 at
Haverthwaite. At SD 356779, just before reaching Holker Park, turn
right onto the minor road and continue to Park Head (SD 336787)
where there is a car park. Here the road continues as a footpath, which
turns south after 200m, keeping close to the base of the low cliff. The
path passes through a gate and the quarried limestone cliffs of Barker
Scar are located immediately to the left. Unit i of the Dalton Beds
crops out at eye level just beyond the old quarry. Each of the units in
this exposure is labelled with a letter.

   None of the sops of Low Furness is now mined. All have
experienced collapse and many are now filled with water.
Nevertheless, a visit to the area is worthwhile to gain an impression
of the nature and situation of these features. Take the A590 from
Ulverston towards Barrow-in-Furness and pass north of Dalton. At
SD 208740, turn right onto the minor road signposted to Sandscale
Haws Nature Reserve. Follow the road to the Nature Reserve, where
there is a car park. Leave the Reserve on foot and return along the
minor road for 1km. At SD 207746, take the track to the left to reach
the largest of the sops, Park. Outcrops of the Park Limestone are
visible in the walls of the flooded pit.

White Scar lies on the southern end of the imposing limestone block of Whitbarrow. To reach the site, follow the A590 from Levens towards Lindale. At SD 466850, just after passing the junction with the A5074, turn right onto the minor road and fork right after 350m towards Raven's Lodge Farm (SD 461852). Immediately beyond the farm, the road bends to the right. Follow the track to the left on foot up the slope to the gate into the quarry. Continue through the quarry. The sites are located on and near the bedrock floor of the old quarry.

GLACIAL ENTRENCHMENT

The location of the Morecambe Bay area on the southern fringe of the Cumbrian massif has meant that the karst of the area has experienced successive episodes of glaciation during the Quaternary. Glacial overdeepening along the Lyth Valley between Whitbarrow and Underbarrow (Figure 2) appears to have produced a bedrock basin in excess of 80m deep. Elsewhere, step-and-stair relief and striated surfaces testify to the role of glacial scour in landscape modification.

As with any erosional feature, it is difficult to establish the age and rate of formation of the glaciated valleys of the Morecambe Bay area. However, the fact that the trenches cut through limestone terrain provides us with a rare opportunity to estimate the extent of valley entrenchment, at least during the most recent glacial stage. In a karst hydrological system, waters draining through the aquifer open up the rock by solution to form caves (although many of these may not be large enough for humans to enter). The waters flowing through these caves return to the surface at the lowest topographic outlet to the aquifer. In other words, they form springs and resurgence caves at the lowest position at which limestone crops out in the valley. If an episode of valley entrenchment now occurs – as a result of glaciation, for example – the spring line will be lowered and the old resurgence caves will be abandoned and left hanging on the valley side.

It has proved possible to determine the hang of a number of fossil resurgence caves above the present spring line in the Morecambe Bay karst (Table 3). Even if we assume glaciation to have been the major agent of valley entrenchment in the area, it is clear that the maximum amount of valley lowering that can have taken place in the last glacial stage is only 9-27m. These figures are based on the assumption that the caves in Table 3 all functioned as active resurgences during the last interglacial stage. Yet the caves may have been abandoned long before this and the rate of valley lowering may be far less than these values indicate. Finally, our estimate of last cold stage incision would be further reduced if we took into account any interglacial entrenchment that may have occurred.

It is apparent that glacial erosion has had little impact on the valleys of south Cumbria. The widely held belief (see, for example, King, 1976; Moseley, 1978) that the landscape of the area is largely the product of last glacial events is clearly very difficult to sustain. The valleys must have existed in their present locations and with essentially their present forms well back into the Quaternary. These results challenge conventional ideas about the efficacy of ice as an

Table 3: The heights of abandoned resurgence caves above present resurgence levels in the Morecambe Bay area

Cave	Location	Approximate height above present resurgence level (*metres*)
Fairy Caves	Humphrey Head	21
The Grand Arch	Humphrey Head	26
Kirkhead Cave	Kirkhead Hill	27
Pool Bank Cave	Whitbarrow	9
Lyth Valley Cave	Whitbarrow	15
Badger Hole	Warton Crag	22
Barrow Scout Cave 1	Warton Crag	9
Barrow Scout Cave 2	Warton Crag	16

Note: Only those situations where the limestone is brought up against impermeable beds and where the present resurgence level can be clearly defined are considered.

agent of erosion. They also contradict the traditional portrayal of upland areas as essentially young and dynamic landscapes in which the preservation potential of ancient relief elements is very limited.

Access

Details of how to obtain access to The Grand Arch are given on page 26. Most of the other caves listed in Table 3 lie in difficult to locate woodland situations or are small and unprepossessing. An excellent example of a glacially-modified trough is the Lyth Valley. The form of the valley and the step-and-stair relief which is a product of glacial scour may be seen by following the A5074 road north from its junction with the A590 Levens to Lindale road at SD 471853.

QUATERNARY HIGH SEA-LEVELS

A series of erosion surface remnants has been identified by Professor Parry (1960) in the karst area surrounding Morecambe Bay. The highest of these, at 213-290m OD, was regarded as a 'partial peneplain', whilst below it the products of ten marine **stillstands** were recognised. Later workers attempted to relate the altitude of a wide range of landforms to these sea-levels. Wave-cut notches, marine benches and sea caves were cited as direct evidence of marine stillstands, and dolines, poljes and cave systems, all apparently constrained within well-defined height ranges, were interpreted as associated with former water tables in the limestone. Unfortunately, no morphological evidence for the sea-levels postulated by Parry has been discovered (Gale, 1981). Many of the wave-cut notches referred to by previous workers cannot be found on the ground and no evidence of them is shown on the large-scale topographic maps of the region. In those cases where notches and benches can be identified they are often structurally controlled and have a form incompatible with that of a wave-cut origin. Thus, 'Quarrying of frost scree breccia' on Whitbarrow (SD 460852) was said to have 'revealed a well-developed [wave-cut] notch at 30m' (Ashmead, 1974, p. 223). Yet inspection of this feature reveals that it is a glacially striated

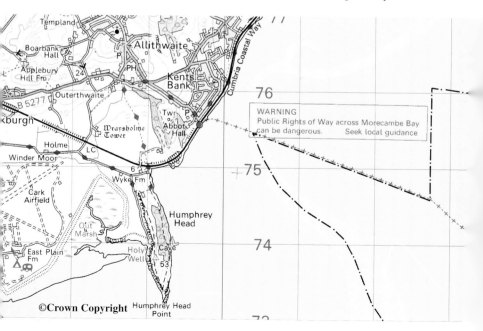

©**Crown Copyright**

Photo 6: The Grand Arch and its associated doline on the western side of
Humphrey Head. Photo: Stephen Gale.

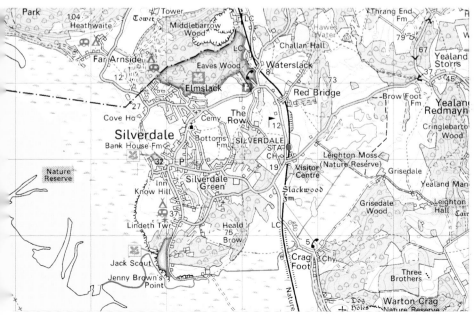

bedding plane dipping at approximately 10° to the north-east, rather than seaward to the south (pages 18 and 19 and Photos 4 and 5).

All those landforms in the Morecambe Bay area previously interpreted as sea caves contain diagnostic features of solutional erosion under **phreatic** conditions, such as solution pockets and phreatic inlets. Furthermore, more accurate measurement of cave altitudes indicates that the caves do not occur at heights coincident with those proposed for marine stillstands. Finally, the observed altitudinal distribution of caves does not differ significantly from that expected given a uniform distribution of caves over the area (Gale, 1981).

The Grand Arch is regarded by proponents of the high Quaternary sea-level thesis as one of the most telling pieces of evidence in support of their case. The Grand Arch (SD 390738) is a dramatic cave formed at an altitude of 34m OD in the sea cliffs along the western side of Humphrey Head (Photo 6). The Head is a fault-bound limestone block lying to the south of Hampsfell. It forms an impressive headland protruding a kilometre into Morecambe Bay. The cave is interpreted by Peter Ashmead (1974) and Professor Tooley (1985) as an unequivocal example of a sea cave, possessing a 'blowhole [which] extends for 12m to a wave-cut platform at 45m' (Ashmead, 1974, p. 224). Yet the cave entrance faces north-north-west, despite the westerly aspect of the marine cliff in which it is situated and the prevailing fetch from the south-west. The 'blowhole' shows a remarkable similarity to the potholes and associated dolines characteristic of true karst caves. Furthermore, the cave possesses features, such as phreatic inlets and solution pockets, which are indicative of solutional erosion under phreatic conditions.

Given the proposed marine origin of The Grand Arch, the cave might be expected to contain sedimentary evidence of marine conditions. Instead, the deposits found in the main phreatic inlet to The Grand Arch consists of **flowstone** overlying clastic colluvial deposits. Further confirmation of the non-marine origin of the clastic beds is provided by the presence of terrestrial faunal remains. The land snails, *Oxychilus cellarius, Discus rotundatus* and *Retinella nitidula,* all occur in cave deposits in Britain, but are restricted to inactive caves and are characteristic of neither freshwater nor marine conditions. Much the same conclusions may be drawn from the remains of field vole and shrew found in the deposits.

Access and safety

From Grange-over-Sands, take the B5277 south-west towards Flookburgh and turn south onto the minor road at SD 381761. Cross the level-crossing and take the next turning on the left. Continue to the end of the road at Humphrey Head. The entrance to The Grand Arch and its associated shaft can be easily seen high up in the cliffs on the west side of Humphrey Head, 90m south of Holy Well.

Access to the cave itself, either from the foot of the cliffs or from the top of the hill, should not be attempted.

THE DEEPDALE DOLINES

Dolines are enclosed karst depressions ranging in diameter from a few metres to over a kilometre. They are usually circular to sub-circular in plan and may reach depths of several hundred metres. Dolines have long been regarded as the fundamental unit of karst relief and many geomorphologists have considered them to be *the* diagnostic karst landform. Dolines may form in a number of ways:

1. They may result from the focusing of solution at the ground surface. This may take place either where surface flow is channelled onto the karst or where runoff is concentrated around a point of leakage beneath a perched **epikarstic aquifer.**
2. The ground may collapse into sub-surface karstic cavities or sag as a result of progressive sub-surface solution.
3. Where the karst is overlain by **regolith**, the solutional widening of sub-surface fractures may result in the loss of unconsolidated overburden down the resultant pipes.

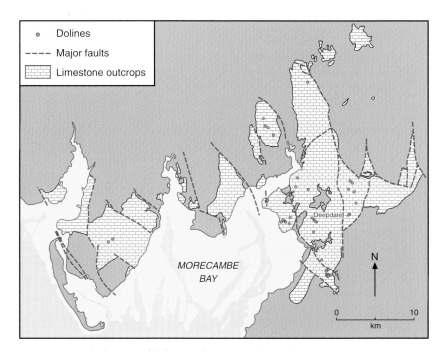

Figure 7: The location of dolines in the Morecambe Bay karst.

In practice, these processes often interact and individual dolines may result from a complex combination of mechanisms.

The Morecambe Bay karst possesses very few dolines, and depression density is considerably less than that observed in most other temperate karsts (Figure 7). One explanation of this is that successive episodes of glacial scour have removed the upper surface of the limestone, and with it any small or incipient depressions. Yet many of the depressions in the region reach impressively large dimensions. These represent probably the greatest assemblage of large dolines known in the British Isles, with the largest being comparable in size to the greatest in the world.

The largest of the Morecambe Bay dolines is Three Brothers (SD 4973), located on top of Warton Crag. This is approximately 440m long and 370m wide. More interesting, however, is the doline complex of Deepdale (SD 4974) on the northern flanks of Warton Crag (Figure 7). The Deepdale dolines consist of a set of four depressions, the largest of which has a maximum diameter of approximately 230m and reaches a depth of approximately 25m (Figure 8). The dolines are aligned and elongated along a north-west to south-east axis and there is evidence that the entire assemblage is developed along a north-west to south-east fault with a downthrow to the north-east. Thus the complex possesses a marked cross-sectional asymmetry, with cliffs and steep slopes to the south-west and gentler slopes to the north-east. Furthermore, the assemblage lies parallel to at least three faults further south on Warton Crag, including the south-easterly continuation of the Silverdale Disturbance, locally named the Warton Crag Fault (Figure 2).

Faults can have a variety of effects on sub-surface drainage in limestone, most of which encourage groundwater flow either along or adjacent to the fault. As a result, solution, cavity formation and collapse take place preferentially along fault lines. The common surface expression of these processes is lines of closed depressions such as those seen at Deepdale.

The bottom of the largest of the closed depressions supports a peat-filled pond, an unusual feature in a karst terrain. The pond has been colonised by willow (*Salix cinerea cinerea*) woodland. Cores of sediment taken from the pond show that over a metre of loess underlies the pond deposits. The loess must have sealed the base of the pond and prevented its waters from leaking into the underlying aquifer. Reworked loess in the entrance to Kirkhead Cave (SD 391756), located on the southern tip of Hampsfell (Figure 2), has been dated to around 11 000 years old (Gale and Hunt, 1985). This may provide a minimum age for loess deposits (such as those at Deepdale) found elsewhere on the karst. The Morecambe Bay loess is thus likely to be of late last glacial age and to have been blown onshore from the complex pro-glacial environment known to have existed after about 18 000 years ago in Morecambe Bay itself (Vincent and Lee, 1981; Gale and Hunt, 1985).

Is there any means by which we might establish the age of the

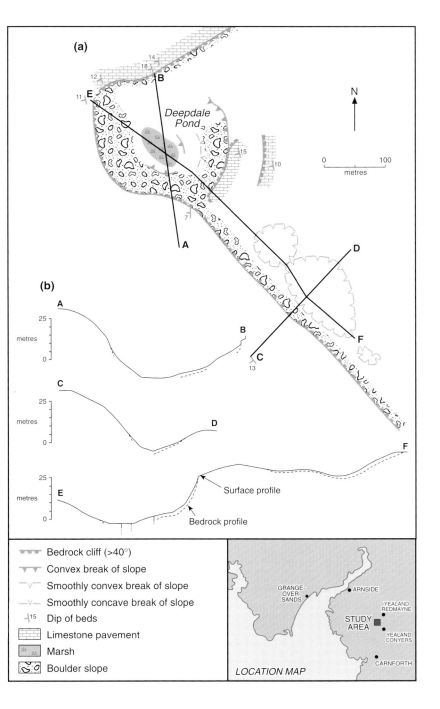

Figure 8: The Deepdale doline complex: (a) the geomorphology and structural dip, and (b) the long and cross profiles and bedrock form. The form of the buried bedrock surface was determined by augering and refraction seismic survey.

largest doline at Deepdale and, by inference, that of the other large depressions of the Morecambe Bay karst? As with all erosional landforms, dolines are difficult to date and geomorphologists are often obliged to use indirect methods to answer questions of this sort. One approach is to investigate any deposits intimately associated with the feature. In this case, the sediments trapped in the doline clearly post-date its formation and thus provide a minimum value for its age. Unfortunately, this allows us to demonstrate only that the feature is of last glacial age or earlier.

An alternative approach, though one beset by difficulties, is to estimate the time required for the formation of the doline by the extrapolation of current rates of geomorphic activity. In the case of the largest of the dolines at Deepdale, an approximate volume of limestone of 0.5 million cubic metres has been removed, equivalent to a mean thickness of 16 metres of rock over the entire area of the doline. Current mean annual rates of limestone solution in England and Wales range between 16 and 102 cubic metres per square kilometre, that is, a mean rate of surface lowering of 16-102 metres per million years. This would place the time of initiation of the doline at between 150 000 and 1 million years ago. In other words, the doline may have begun forming some time between the Early Quaternary and the penultimate glacial. This is therefore a landform of some antiquity. Yet, as has already been pointed out (page 22), it has been widely assumed that all elements of the Cumbrian landscape are youthful and that only fragments of the ancient relief can have escaped obliteration by glacial scour during the last cold stage. The fact that this is not the case shows, once again, not only that the preservation potential of ancient landforms is far greater than has previously been accepted, but also that the impact of glacial scour on the landscape of the area was far less than is conventionally believed.

It is instructive to consider the assumptions which we must make in order to undertake the calculations discussed above.

1. *The entire volume of the doline has been removed by dissolution.* It is possible that other karstic processes, such as collapse, may have contributed to the formation of the depression. However, since these are also a product of localised solution, their contribution to doline formation is subsumed within the solution rates determined for the site as a whole. It is unlikely that any non-karstic mechanisms have contributed significantly to the enlargement of the doline.

2. *The measured size of the doline represents the total volume of rock removed.* The existence of a sediment infill means that the measured volume can only be a minimum figure. Nevertheless, except in the base of the depression, the deposits simply form a veneer over the bedrock and contribute little to the form of the basin. More difficult to judge is the extent to which lowering of the basin rim has occurred since the doline began to form. The planar

nature of the doline rim, however, suggests that the original surface into which the depression was eroded is still essentially intact.

3. *Rates of solution at the site have not changed over time and are the same as those prevailing at present.* This assumption is highly unlikely to be correct given that the present time is one of immense environmental disturbance and that large, rapid and frequent environmental shifts are known to have taken place throughout the Quaternary. Indeed, most evidence indicates that direct measurements of modern processes yield rates that are perhaps an order of magnitude greater than the long-term mean rates.

4. *Rates of solution determined elsewhere in England and Wales are comparable with those prevailing at Deepdale.* The range of values used to estimate the denudation rate covers almost an order of magnitude. Moreover, this range is very similar to those obtained from temperate, alpine and sub-arctic karsts worldwide. It is very unlikely that solution rates at Deepdale fall outside these limits.

This discussion indicates that, if anything, our assumptions are conservative; that is, long-term rates of geomorphic activity are likely to be lower and the volume of rock removed is likely to be higher than assumed. The estimated age of the largest doline at Deepdale is therefore likely to be a minimum one.

Access

Take the road from Yealand Redmayne towards Warton. Turn right at SD 503743 and follow the road uphill for 125m to a sharp bend to the left. Pass through the stile on the right of the road and follow the vehicle track to a gate. A few metres to the left of this gate is a small pedestrian gate in the fence. Pass through this and follow the path through the woods to a stile. Beyond this, a track crosses an open field containing the two central dolines of the Deepdale complex. On the far side of the field, the track passes through a gate. To the left of this is a stile over a fence. Cross the stile and follow the path down through the woodlands into the main depression.

KARST HYDROLOGY AT DUNALD MILL HOLE

Throughout most of the Morecambe Bay karst, the Urswick Limestone forms the highest rocks, both stratigraphically and topographically. As a result of the high permeability of this unit, almost all the groundwater recharge is by **diffuse flow.** By contrast, in the Kellet area, the Early Carboniferous Gleaston Formation and the Late Carboniferous sandstone overlie the limestone (Figure 9). Not only does this result in surface water flow across impermeable lithologies and the possibility of concentrated flow input to the karst, it also means a focusing of solutional activity and the potential development of large-scale karst features. The geological structure of the Kellet area also differs from that of the rest of the Morecambe Bay karst. In contrast to the fault-bound, **cuesta-**like blocks of the rest of the region, the rocks of the Kellet area have been folded into a plunging anticline and truncated by an undulating erosion surface. The most important result of this from a hydrological point of view is that the limestone is surrounded by a fringe of impermeable rocks. In general, the limestone constitutes the higher ground in the area. This means that the limestone-Gleaston Formation boundary tends to form a spring line for karst groundwaters, with a less significant line of springs occurring along the contact between the Gleaston Formation and the overlying Late Carboniferous sandstone (Figure 9).

At Dunald Mill Hole (SD 515676) near Nether Kellet, however, this hydrological situation is reversed. The limestone is topographically lower than the fringing impermeable beds and waters flowing off the rocks of the Gleaston Formation sink into an impressive cave entrance soon after meeting the limestone (Figure 9). Dunald Mill Hole forms the end of a blind valley which has resulted, in part, from the progressive collapse of the former cave entrance.

The route taken by the water after sinking at Dunald Mill Hole is poorly known, but at least part of the flow resurges about 3.5km to the north at Netherbeck Spring (SD 508709) near Netherbeck Farm. During floods, both Backlane Quarry Cave (SD 504694) and Brewer's Barn Hole (SD 508705) act as overflows for the Dunald Mill system (Figure 9).

Underground, the system consists of two main components: the active stream passage, Dunald Mill Hole, and a higher level, inactive system, Dunald Mill Cave. The two cave systems are approximately parallel. It is likely that the upper passage, Dunald Mill Cave, formed an earlier drainage route whose waters were subsequently captured by the development of Dunald Mill Hole.

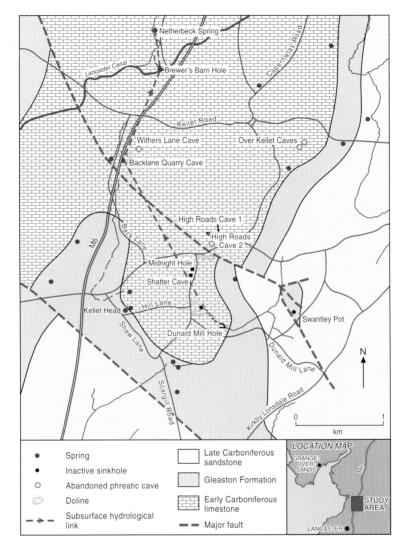

Figure 9: The geology and karst hydrology of the Kellet area.

Access and safety

Leave the B6254 at Over Kellet to follow the minor road south towards Nether Kellet. Turn left at SD 513685 and turn left again immediately after the quarries for 330m to Dunald Mill Cottage (SD 515675). The cave entrance lies in the bottom of the valley immediately to the left of the road.

Dunald Mill Hole is potentially dangerous and should be descended only by properly trained and equipped parties.

HAWES WATER POLJE

The large-scale enclosed depressions known as poljes are rarely found in the British Isles. However, several of the mosses of the Morecambe Bay karst might qualify for such a definition. A polje is a large, flat-floored closed basin, one or more of whose sides rise steeply from its base. The drainage of poljes consists of groundwater and/or surface water inflow and karstic outflow. A positive imbalance between these two components results in the intermittent or perennial inundation of the polje floor. Under these conditions, surface water overflow from the basin may occur.

Probably the best example of a polje in the Morecambe Bay region is Hawes Water (SD 4776) (Photo 7 and Figure 10). This is a flat-floored depression, 0.39 square kilometres in area, surrounded by relatively steeply-rising slopes and located entirely within the karst. Hawes Water falls within the category referred to by Professor Gams (1978) as 'poljes in the piezometric level'. These are features developed entirely on karst rocks in which the polje floor is located within the range of fluctuation of the water table. This means that the basin is flooded during times of high groundwater levels. Both inflow to and outflow from such poljes are largely karstic.

Photo 7: The northern end of the flat-floored enclosed depression of Hawes Water *showing the steeply-rising limestone hills which form the eastern margin of the polje. Photo: Peter Crooks.*

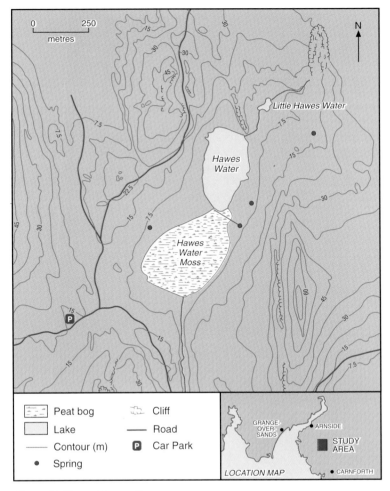

Figure 10: Hawes Water polje.

As with several other mosses in the Morecambe Bay area, Hawes Water is located along the line of the Silverdale Disturbance (Figure 2): enhanced erosion along the fault zone is likely to have encouraged the development of the basin. The polje is floored by lacustrine sediments and supports two permanent water bodies (Hawes Water and Little Hawes Water at SD 479768) which expand in area at times of high groundwater levels. The deposition of impermeable sediments in the basin has created an interior fluviolacustrine plain in the karst.

Under normal conditions, a series of marginal springs discharges water into the basin, but the lake levels are essentially maintained by the regional water table. The lakes form where the groundwater system intersects the ground surface, and the entire basin forms a window on the underlying water table. At Red Bridge (SD 475757), a surface water outlet cuts across a low rock bar. However, this functions only to conduct overflow during times of high lake levels. Apart from evapotranspirative losses, the bulk of the discharge from the polje must therefore be karstic in nature, the result of seepage from the lake into the underlying aquifer.

Access

From Carnforth, take the A6 north towards Milnthorpe. At SD 512757, turn left onto the minor road and follow the signs to Silverdale. Cross the railway and turn immediately right. Follow the road to the car park at Eaves Wood (SD 470759). From the car park walk back along the road to the footpath at SD 472759. The footpath may be followed around the lake by way of Challan Hall, joining Moss Lane at SD 479763 and returning to the Silverdale road at Red Bridge (SD 474758).

THE LIMESTONE PAVEMENTS OF HUTTON ROOF CRAGS

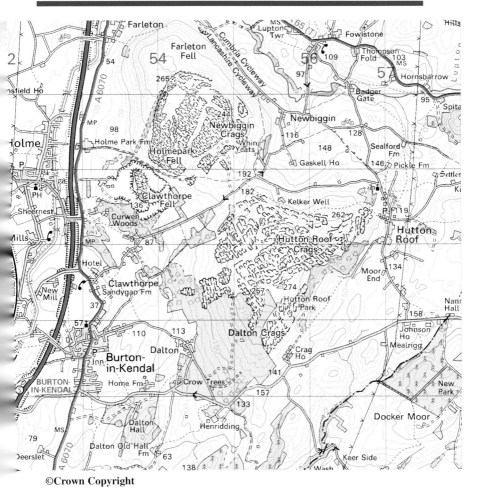

The limestone pavements of Hutton Roof Crags (SD 5678) (Photo 8) are amongst the best known in Britain. As with all the well-developed pavements in the Morecambe Bay karst, those on Hutton Roof are formed on the pure, hard and compact, massively bedded and widely jointed Urswick Limestone. Hutton Roof Crags lie immediately to the west of the Hutton Roof Disturbance (Figure 2), with the result that the limestones hereabouts dip east at 20-28°.

Pavements can develop in a wide range of karstic environments. The main requirements are:

Photo 8: The limestone pavements of Hutton Roof Crags. Photo: Stephen Gale.

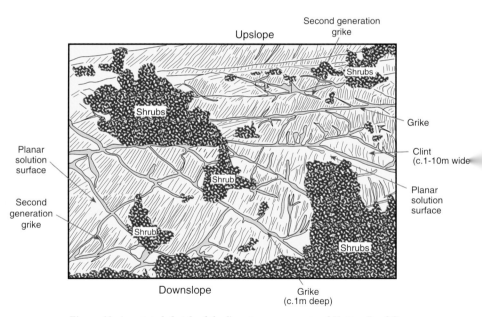

Figure 11: Annotated sketch of the limestone pavements of Hutton Roof Crags shown in Photo 8, depicting various karren forms.

1. The availability of some mechanism to strip overburden or weathered rock from the karst surface.
2. The existence of rocks capable of supporting solutional sculpture.

The most probable mechanism of stripping in north-west England would appear to have been glacial scour during the most recent glacial stage. However, there is considerable evidence to suggest that pavements in the area are rapidly colonised by vegetation when left undisturbed (Burgess and Mitchell, 1994). The maintenance and, indeed, the initial exposure of the limestone surface may therefore be a result of activities such as grazing or deforestation.

The small-scale solutional features formed on karst surfaces are referred to as karren. The primary karren forms on Hutton Roof are grikes (Photo 8 and Figure 11): linear solutional features which develop along fractures in the rock. They have high length:width ratios and are of the order of a metre deep. Three joint sets have been opened by solution on Hutton Roof (Figure 12). These intersect to form isolated, diamond shaped blocks, or clints, each of the order of metres wide (Photo 8 and Figure 11).

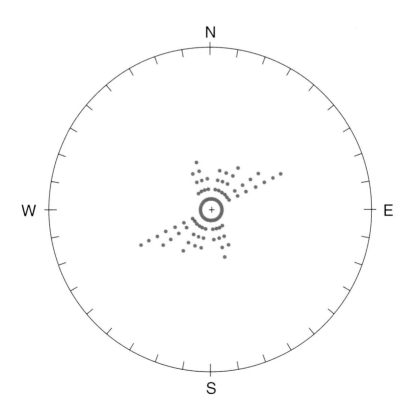

Figure 12: The orientation of solutionally opened joints on Hutton Roof Crags *(n = 50).*

Photo 9: Clint surfaces at Hutton Roof Crags. *The upslope planar solution surfaces and their replacement downslope by rinnenkarren are clearly visible. The knife is 90mm long. Photo: Stephen Gale.*

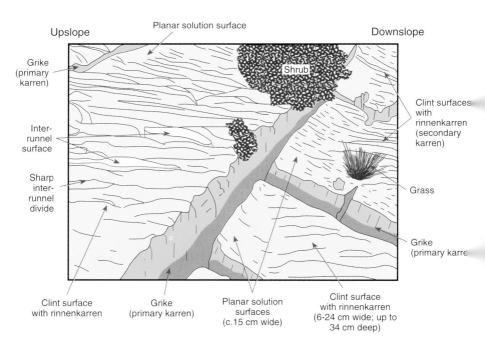

Figure 13: Annotated sketch of the clint surfaces at Hutton Roof Crags shown in Photo 9, *depicting various karren forms.*

The clints support a range of secondary karren features. On their upper edges are found planar solution surfaces (Photo 9 and Figure 13). These appear to be the product of sheetflow across the upslope part of the clint surface: under these conditions, solution is likely to be relatively evenly distributed across the surface. Downslope, the planar solution surfaces are replaced by rinnenkarren (Photo 9 and Figure 13). These are sub-parallel solutional runnels with rounded cross-sections, largely between 6cm and 24cm wide and up to 34cm deep. The rinnenkarren on Hutton Roof reach lengths of at least 13.15m – perhaps the longest recorded in the world (see frontispiece). Where the runnels are close packed, they are generally separated by sharp divides. Where there is space between adjacent runnels, however, the interfluves may be sub-planar or sub-rounded. These inter-runnel surfaces may be sufficiently wide that further rinnenkarren are able to develop on them.

Several workers have asserted that the catchment areas and thus the discharge of rinnenkarren increase downstream, and that the channels therefore normally become wider and deeper with distance downslope. This is not necessarily the case at Hutton Roof, where many runnels reach a maximum depth midway along their channels. This may indicate that channel size is a function of solutional potential rather than hydraulic control as in the case of conventional open-channel flow. Likewise, the downstream width of individual channels tends to be relatively constant. This is probably the result of competition for space amongst closely packed channels. Occasionally, the deeper channels on Hutton Roof may significantly increase their width by expanding into and capturing adjacent, shallower, channels.

Although rinnenkarren are common features of limestone pavements, surprisingly little is known of either their form or the processes of their formation. Dr Glew and Professor Ford (1980) have stated that rinnenkarren develop where runoff on the planar solution surface reaches an unstable thickness and breaks down to turbulent flow. The implication of this is that runoff in the sheetflow zone across the upslope part of the clint surface is laminar. Yet it has been recognised since at least the time of Horton (1945) that this is not the case. A more likely cause of the change from planar to channelled solution is lateral flow concentration in the sheetflow zone. This can occur within about 15cm of the drainage divide (Emmett, 1978). Such sub-parallel zones of more rapid flow, developed normal to the contours, will experience higher rates of solution. As a result, solutional runnels will develop which in turn will capture surrounding waters, further enhancing dissolution rates along the channels.

Almost every clint on this part of Hutton Roof Crags possesses a planar solution surface on its updip edge and solutional runnels draining its downdip slopes. No example has been observed of a primary grike cutting across either the planar solution surface or the rinnenkarren. The secondary karren features must therefore post-date grike formation.

A second generation of grikes is currently developing on the clint surfaces. These are aligned along joints, but taper at one or both ends to form closed features. It is likely that further solution will see these secondary grikes extend laterally to intersect the surrounding primary grikes, transforming the second generation forms into open features and isolating smaller clint blocks. The secondary grikes cut through the solutional runnels and must therefore post-date them. However, towards the open (that is, the older) ends of many of the closed grikes, planar solution surfaces have already replaced rinnenkarren on the downslope side of the grike. This is indicative of the rapid development of karren at this site and the speedy obliteration of earlier solutional forms.

Dr Sweeting (1972) suggested that the channels found at Hutton Roof are actually rounded runnels (or rundkarren), originally developed under a soil cover, but sharpened by solution of the bare rock. Indeed, she has argued that no true rinnenkarren occur in Britain. But the planar solution surfaces which drain into the runnels appear to form only under free atmospheric conditions. Since the planar surfaces and the runnels appear to be genetically related, then the runnels at Hutton Roof must also be sub-aerially formed. If we assume that the runnels are indeed exhumed features, then any trace of pre-existing rundkarren on the upslope edge of the clint must already have been obliterated by the surface lowering which has given rise to the planar solution surface. Given this, it is difficult to accept that any element of the original rundkarren can have survived surface lowering elsewhere on the clint.

The eminent hydrologist, Robert Horton (1945), proposed that, during rainstorms, sheetflow occurs over the upper parts of hillslopes. Adjacent to the drainage divide, the flow is shallow and has insufficient energy to erode the surface. The top part of a slope is therefore characterised by a 'belt of no erosion'. Downslope, catchment area and discharge increase, as does flow depth. As a result, the stress imparted by the flow on the bed also increases and sheet erosion begins. Accidental flow concentrations, perhaps the result of irregularities in the slope, cause flow focusing, an increase in flow depth and the initiation of scour. Channels begin to be eroded into the slope. These capture discharge from upstream, resulting in the headward extension of channels to the downslope limit of the belt of no erosion. Thus, the belt of no erosion is succeeded downslope by a zone of rill development.

At first sight, it would appear that the downslope change from a planar solution surface to a surface channelled by parallel rills represents a classic example of Horton's model of hillslope erosion. Despite their similarities, however, these features cannot be the same as those developed on hillslopes. The karren are the products of solution and not mechanical erosion. There is therefore no reason why the formation of rinnenkarren should occur only when flows exceed a certain critical level of shear stress. Furthermore, the evidence at Hutton Roof and the experiments of Glew and Ford (1980) demonstrate that solutional erosion occurs across the planar solution surface. The planar zone close to the drainage divide cannot therefore represent a 'belt of no erosion' as indicated by the Hortonian model (1945).

Access

Hutton Roof can be reached from the west by taking the turning towards Whittington off the A6070 at the southern end of Burton-in-Kendal. Follow the road to SD 572769 and turn left to Hutton Roof village. Alternatively, follow the B6254 south from the A65 at Kirkby Lonsdale. Turn right at Whittington along the road to Burton-in-Kendal. Turn right at SD 572769 to Hutton Roof village.

Almost opposite the turning to Kirkby Lonsdale in the middle of Hutton Roof village is a path leading uphill between two houses. Follow this. Pass through a gate and take the left-hand fork by the highest cottage. Follow the main path uphill through the bracken. Much of Hutton Roof Crags is worth exploring, but the sites described here lie to the left of the path just beyond the first limestone ridge.

GLOSSARY

Blind valley. A valley closed at its downstream end. It is formed as the result of a sinking stream enlarging its underground course and entrenching its valley to such an extent that no flow occurs beyond the sink point.

Breccia. A rock composed largely of angular fragments of previously existing rock greater than 2mm in diameter.

Clastic. Composed of detrital material such as pebbles, sands or muds.

Cuesta. A landform resulting from the differential erosion of an interbedded sequence of gently dipping sedimentary rocks of differing resistance. The more resistant beds are left upstanding as asymmetrical, strike-aligned uplands composed of a long, gentle back slope and a short, steep scarp slope.

Diffuse flow. The flow of water into an aquifer via many of the inlets across an outcrop. Diffuse recharge is derived solely from direct precipitation onto the aquifer.

Doline. An enclosed karstic depression formed by localised solution and/or subsidence into sub-surface karstic cavities.

Dolomitisation/Dolomitised. Dolomite rock is composed of high magnesium calcite. Dolomitisation occurs when a limestone (a rock composed largely of calcite) is converted to a dolomite. There is a variety of mechanisms by which this may occur.

Epikarstic aquifer. The bulk of the solution in most karst systems takes place in the top few metres of the rock. This opens up fissures to produce a high permeability aquifer just below the ground surface. This is the epikarstic aquifer. The groundwater system is therefore composed of a high permeability epikarstic aquifer overlying a lower permeability karst aquifer. Recharge to the epikarstic aquifer is efficient, but discharge is relatively inefficient. The epikarstic aquifer is thus able to store water which leaks slowly into the underlying karst.

Flowstone. A carbonate precipitate deposited from percolation waters flowing down the roof, walls and across the floor of caves.

Interstices. The intervening spaces between the materials of which rocks and other geological substances are composed.

Karst. A landscape produced by the solutional action of water as it passes over or through highly soluble bedrock. The opening up of the rock by solution leads to the progressive replacement of surface by underground drainage.

Limestone pavement. A bare karstic surface, divided into a geometrical pattern of blocks (clints) by the intersection of solutionally-widened fissures (grikes). The angle of the surface is approximately parallel to that of the bedding.

Loess. A fine grained, windblown deposit typically composed of massively-bedded, coarse silts. Most loess has a periglacial origin.

Moss. A term used in north-west England to describe a large, low altitude peat bog.

Palaeokarst surface. A karst surface which has been preserved by burial and which is no longer part of the active karst system.

Phreatic. Beneath the level of groundwater saturation. Phreatic caves therefore develop under pipefull flow conditions and flow occurs under hydrostatic pressure.

Polje. A large, flat-floored enclosed basin, one or more of whose sides rise steeply from its base. Its drainage consists of groundwater and/or surface water inflow and karstic outflow.

Pseudobreccia. An irregularly recrystallised or partly dolomitised limestone in which the selective growth of coarse crystals gives the rock an apparently fragmented texture.

Regolith. The mantle of unconsolidated material on the Earth's surface, whatever its nature or origin.

Rock pendant. A smooth, stalactite-like bedrock projection resulting from the differential solution of a cave roof.

Sheetflow. Shallow, laterally-extensive, unchannelled water flow.

Sinkhole (see Figure 9). A surface depression or opening where concentrated surface flow sinks underground.

Slickensided. Polished and/or striated by the friction generated as one rock slides against another during faulting.

Stillstand. A period during which mean sea-levels remain constant.

Terra rossa. A red soil developed on fine grained, iron oxide rich material overlying limestone bedrock. The fine material was formerly thought to represent the weathering residue of the limestone. These soils are particularly well-developed in areas of Mediterranean climate.

BIBLIOGRAPHY

Ashmead, P. (1974) 'The caves and karst of the Morecambe Bay area' in Waltham, A.C. (ed) *The Limestones and Caves of North-West England*. Newton Abbot: David & Charles, pp. 201-26.

Burgess, I.C. and Mitchell, M. (1994) 'Origin of limestone pavements', *The Proceedings of the Cumberland Geological Society*, 5, pp. 405-12.

Corbel, J. (1957) 'Les karsts du nord-ouest de l'Europe et de quelques régions de comparaison étude sur le role du climat dans l'erosion des calcaires', *Institut des Études Rhodaniennes de l'Université de Lyon Mémoires et Documents*, 12, pp. 1-541.

Emmett, W.W. (1978) 'Overland flow' in Kirkby, M.J. (ed) *Hillslope Hydrology*. Chichester: Wiley, pp. 145-76.

Gale, S.J. (1981) 'The geomorphology of the Morecambe Bay karst and its implications for landscape chronology', *Zeitschrift für Geomorphologie*, NF, 25, pp. 457-69.

Gale, S.J. and Hunt, C.O. (1985) 'The stratigraphy of Kirkhead Cave, an upper palaeolithic site in northern England', *Proceedings of the Prehistoric Society*, 51, pp. 283-304.

Gams, I. (1978) 'The polje: the problem of definition', *Zeitschrift für Geomorphologie*, NF, 22, pp. 170-81.

Glew, J.R. and Ford, D.C. (1980) 'A simulation study of the development of rillenkarren', *Earth Surface Processes*, 5, pp. 25-36.

Horton, R.E. (1945) 'Erosional development of streams and their drainage basins; hydrophysical approach to quantitative morphology', *Bulletin of the Geological Society of America*, 56, pp. 275-370.

King, C.A.M. (1976) *Northern England*. London: Methuen.

Moseley, F. (1978) *The Geology of the Lake District*. Yorkshire Geological Society Occasional Publication, 3.

Parry, J.T. (1960) 'The erosion surfaces of the south-western Lake District', *The Institute of British Geographers Transactions and Papers*, 28, pp. 39-54.

Rose, W.C.C. and Dunham, K.C. (1977) 'Geology and hematite deposits of South Cumbria', *Economic Memoir of the Geological Survey of Great Britain*, Sheets 58 and part 48.

Rose, W.C.C., Dunham, K.C. and Evans, W.B. (1977) *Sheet SD27 (with parts of SD17 and SD37) Dalton-in-Furness 1:25 000*. London: Institute of Geological Sciences.

Sweeting, M.M. (1970) 'Recent developments and techniques in the study of karst landforms in the British Isles', *Geographia Polonica*, 18, pp. 227-41.

Sweeting, M.M. (1972) *Karst Landforms*. London: Macmillan.

Sweeting, M.M. (1973) 'Some problems of relict and fossil karst in England', *Geographische Zeitschrift*, 32, pp. 104-7.

Tooley, M.J. (1985) 'Sea-level changes and coastal morphology in North-west England' in Johnson, R.H. (ed) *The Geomorphology of North-west England*. Manchester: Manchester University Press, pp. 94-121.

Vincent, P.J. (1981) 'Some observations on the so-called relict karst of the Morecambe Bay region, north-west England', *Revue de Géologie Dynamique et de Géographie Physique*, 23, pp. 143-50.

Vincent, P.J. and Lee, M.P. (1981) 'Some observations on the loess around Morecambe Bay, north-west England', *Proceedings of the Yorkshire Geological Society*, 43, pp. 281-94.

BGS resources

Catalogues of BGS's maps, books and other publications are available on request from: Sales Desk, British Geological Survey, Kingsley Dunham Centre, Keyworth, Nottingham NG12 5GG.
Tel: 0115 936 3241; fax: 0115 936 3488.

Examples of the publications can be viewed on the BGS website: http://www.bgs.ac.uk/bgs/products.html